ZERO TOLERANCE

A PLAY BY
ADAM GRANT

SCHOLASTIC INC.
New York Toronto London Auckland Sydney
Mexico City New Delhi Hong Kong Buenos Aires

P9-AOW-055

COVER ILLUSTRATION BY

JOHN RITTER

INTERIOR ILLUSTRATIONS BY

MARK POUTENIS

Originally published in *Scholastic Scope* magazine, April 19, 1996.

10   11   12   23   12 11 10

CHARACTERS

Narrator

Ms. Allen - English teacher

Principal Hodges

Superintendent Webster

Students **Jeremy**
         Caitlin
         Janet
         Mark
         Kevin
         Tomas
         Lisa

Teachers **Ms. Evans**
         Mrs. Crandall
         Mr. Desmond
         Mr. Carney

Mom - Jeremy's mother

What's more important: The rights of one student, or the well-being of the entire school?

Narrator: It is first period on Monday morning in Ms. Allen's English class. Most of the students are getting ready for class and talking quietly. A small group of kids in the back of the room is being very loud—laughing, joking, and generally bothering everyone else.

Ms. Allen: Good morning everyone. Let's get started. Janet and Jeremy, quiet down, please. I hope everyone was able to read the first 30 pages of *Fahrenheit 451*.

Narrator: Most students quiet down and take out their books, but the noise continues from the back of the room.

Ms. Allen: Students in the back, please be quiet. Jeremy, take out your book.

Jeremy: What's it like on your planet, Ms. Alien?

Narrator: Everyone in the back row laughs as

Jeremy starts to talk through his nose, as if he's imitating a Martian.

Jeremy: Take me to your leader, Ms. Alien.

Ms. Allen: Grow up, Jeremy.

Narrator: Ms. Allen has been down this road before with the students in the back row. She tries to lead everyone's attention back to their homework assignment.

Ms. Allen: Now, based on what you've read, who can tell us one of the themes of *Fahrenheit 451*?

Narrator: A student from another area of the room raises her hand.

Ms. Allen: Go ahead, Caitlin.

Caitlin: It's about whether the rights of one person are more important than the rights of the entire society. The main character, Montag, lives in a society where no one has any rights at all. They are not even allowed to read books.

Ms. Allen: Go on. Why would any society make it illegal to read?

Caitlin: Maybe it's because books introduce you to new ideas. People are much easier to control if they are not thinking. Society as a whole runs more smoothly that way, but—

Narrator: Caitlin is interrupted by another voice from the back of the room.

Janet: Hey Caitlin, you look great today. Where did you get that outfit? Librarians R Us?

Narrator: Caitlin's friend Mark speaks up.

Mark: Hey Janet, shut up, will you?

Kevin: You shut up, wimp, before you get hurt.

Ms. Allen: All right, that's enough! Janet, Jeremy, I'm really losing my patience with you. Now, if you don't want an education that's one thing. But I cannot let you prevent the rest of the class from learning anything either.

Jeremy *(whispering)*: Ms. Alien, phone home.

Ms. Allen: I could send you all to the principal's office again, but it never seems to do any good. So I've got a better idea. The next person who talks out of turn is buying the whole class some extra work. Now who would like to read the first three paragraphs out loud? Raise your hands.

Narrator: As Ms. Allen looks away, Kevin gets Mark's attention.

Kevin *(mouthing the words quietly)*: You're mine after school.

Narrator: Kevin opens his jacket to show Mark a knife. Mark can't believe what he's seeing.

Mark *(loudly, to Kevin)*: Are you nuts?

Ms. Allen: That's it! Congratulations, Mark, you just bought yourself and your friends several extra pages of homework.

Mark: But, but I . . . He—

Ms. Allen: Mark, you don't really want to disrupt the whole class again, do you?

Narrator: After class, Caitlin walks up to Ms. Allen's desk.

Caitlin: You know, Kevin was threatening Mark with a knife when you caught him talking. It wasn't Mark's fault.

Ms. Allen: Really? I didn't see that. I suppose that does change things. This is very serious. I'll have to speak to the principal about it. Thanks for telling me, Caitlin.

Jeremy is just looking to have a little fun. But Kevin is looking for trouble. . . .

Narrator: Later that day, Jeremy finds Kevin standing at his locker.

Jeremy: Hey, did you really bring a knife to class?

Kevin: Yeah, I got it from my cousin. Cool, huh?

Jeremy: No, not cool. Are you out of your mind?

Kevin: You should talk. You make more trouble with Ms. Alien than I do.

Jeremy: I'm just trying to have a little fun and get through class. I don't know what you're thinking! You're going to get kicked out of school.

Kevin: What do I care? I don't need this place. I'll get a job. Man, what happened to you? When did you become such a girl?

Jeremy: Give it a rest!

It's official: Discipline is now the school's number one priority.

Narrator: As the regular Monday faculty meeting begins, Principal Hodges calls the room to order.

Principal Hodges: Okay everyone, let's get started. What's on your minds?

Mr. Desmond: I don't know about the rest of you, but in the science lab, my biggest problem by far is still discipline.

Ms. Evans: That's what I wanted to talk about. Some of my kids are out of control.

Principal: Look, we've been talking about this for the last five meetings. Plus, I just got a memo from the district superintendent, telling all the principals to make discipline our number one priority. Now let's put our heads together and do something. Who wants to give me some specifics?

Ms. Allen: I will. I have a group of students in my first period English class who are just impossible.

I've tried separating them, I've tried punishing them. Nothing works.

Mrs. Crandall: Evelyn, you just can't expect the same kind of respect that we used to give our teachers. Kids are different today. Talk to them. Find out what's going on in their home lives. Some of these kids have an awful lot to deal with.

Ms. Allen: Don't you think I've tried to do that? It's too late. I heard that one of them even brought a knife to school.

Mr. Desmond: Evelyn's right. Some of these kids are way too far gone to respond to counseling. They need to face some tough choices. I say kick them right out of school.

Principal: All right, let me give this some thought. I would like all of you to give me a list of the most disruptive kids in your classes—the kids who really cause problems. Then I'll figure out what our options are.

What do you think the school should do about the kids who make trouble?

Principal to students: There is now zero tolerance for troublemakers.

Narrator: That night, Ms. Allen receives a phone call from Principal Hodges.

Principal: Evelyn, I'm sorry to call so late, but I've got good news for you. I took the list you teachers gave me, and I've suspended every kid on the list.

Ms. Allen: You what? You didn't ask us for a list of kids to suspend. You just asked me who was causing trouble! Not all those kids are that bad!

Principal: They can all come back to school if they and their parents meet with me. But it's time to send a message to the students: We're running this school, and they have to follow our rules. We will now have zero tolerance for troublemakers! That's our new policy.

Ms. Allen: Well, Mr. Hodges, I hope it's not too strong a message.

English class is full . . . of empty seats.

Narrator: The next day in Ms. Allen's first-period English class, there are three empty chairs in the back row. Class goes smoothly for the first time in weeks, but Ms. Allen knows that her students are wondering what happened to the other kids.

Ms. Allen: Class, I think you should know that Principal Hodges has suspended Janet, Kevin, and Jeremy, along with 45 other students. If you want to take the rest of this class to voice your opinions, let's do that.

Narrator: An enormous cheer erupts from the class. Every student is standing and clapping except for Caitlin.

Ms. Allen: Okay, settle down everyone. Caitlin, you look like you have something to say.

Caitlin: I think it was wrong to kick them all out.

Mark: Are you nuts? They were just picking on

you yesterday. What do you care about them?

Caitlin: Don't you see? It's just like in *Fahrenheit 451*. When Principal Hodges changed the rules and kicked them out, it was for the good of our little society, but what about Janet, Kevin, and Jeremy's rights?

Tomas: Oh, come on. They knew their behavior was out of line, and they did it anyway.

Caitlin: The other day, the punishment for disrupting class was a trip to the principal's office. Today, they get kicked out of school for it. At the very least, they deserved some kind of hearing. That's the way America works.

Mark: I guess that's true. I wonder what all those other kids did to get kicked out. Everybody would have heard about it if they had done anything all that bad.

Which is more important—the rights of one student or the well-being of the entire school?

Does the punishment fit the crime?

Act 6

Narrator: Jeremy comes home and hands his mother a letter from Principal Hodges.

Jeremy: Mom, I got suspended, and I'm not even sure what I did.

Mom: What are you talking about? Let me see that. It says here that you were disruptive and involved in an incident with a knife. Jeremy, you'd better start talking.

Jeremy: All I did was make some jokes about Ms. Allen, honest. Kevin had a knife, and he sort of showed it to someone. I was just sitting next to him, and I might have made some jokes.

Mom: You've had a big mouth for a long time, pal. That's not news to me. But it's not enough to get you suspended. The punishment is too serious. This will be on your record. You could have trouble getting into college because of this.

Jeremy: I'm glad you can at least see what's going on here. My principal's gone nuts.

Mom: Hold on. I'm going to fight this punishment because it's too extreme, but make no mistake about why this happened. If you treated people with respect, you wouldn't have this problem.

Narrator: Jeremy goes outside and sits on his front steps. He's totally depressed. He sees Kevin walking toward him with a big grin on his face.

Kevin: Summer's here awful early isn't it? What are you going to do with your vacation?

Jeremy: Vacation? Are you kidding? This is awful. My mom is furious. I might miss out on college. Don't your parents care?

Kevin: My father barely knows how old I am. He'll never find out about this. And I can't remember when I saw mom last. This is definitely the best thing that ever happened to me. I don't need school.

Jeremy: What are you going to do?

Kevin: Whatever I want. Party, hang out, watch videos, who cares? One thing's for sure—I'm not going to sit around crying about it like you.

Jeremy: Man, you're really sick.

Does the school really have the right to give up on difficult students?

Act 7

Narrator: That afternoon, Principal Hodges is trying to digest his veal cutlet from lunch when his phone rings. It's his boss.

Superintendent Webster: Hodges, this is Ben Webster calling.

Principal: Superintendent, what a surprise!

Superintendent *(impatient and annoyed)*: Never mind that, Hodges. I've got one question for you. Do you know what I had for lunch today?

Principal: Uh, no sir, I uh . . .

Superintendent: TV cameras, Hodges. TV reporters and newspaper reporters. They all wanted to know if one of my principals had really kicked 48 kids out of school. I told them that there must be some mistake. Was I right?

Principal: Sir, I did suspend 48 students, but I

was justified. I just got your memo about making discipline our number one priority. Also, people all over the country are sick of schools babying kids who are discipline problems. Something had to be done.

Superintendent: Are you out of your mind? Do you know what the papers are going to do to us? And who are you to decide which kids are okay to give up on? You'd better get down here right now and help me figure out how to fix this mess.

The rules changed without warning. Who knows what could get someone suspended next week?

Narrator: Two nights later, parents, teachers, and students all show up for a town meeting at the school gym, eager to have their say. There's also a handful of TV and newspaper reporters.

Principal: Welcome. The purpose of this meeting is to air your opinions about the 48 suspensions at our school. I encourage you all to speak your mind. Who would like to start?

Mom: Hello, I'm Jeremy Stewart's mother, and I've contacted my lawyer. He says it's against the law for you to deny my child an education.

Principal: Your son can get an education—once he's shown me that he's changed his behavior.

Mom: But by the time he gets back into school, he will have missed a lot of classes. Why should he have to work harder than the other students just to pass his classes?

Principal: I removed him from school because he was preventing other students from getting an education. He was violating their rights.

Mom: So you just gave up on him? Just because he's a smart-aleck?

Principal: Look ma'am, your son is a smart-aleck. Someone else's son brings a knife to school. They are different, but both are unacceptable.

Narrator: A student on the other side of the room stands up.

Tomas: Mr. Hodges, I just wanted to say that I'm glad that you did what you did, and a lot of other kids are, too. It's a lot nicer around here since you got rid of all those kids.

Principal: Thank you. *(He pauses.)* Do any teachers have comments?

Mr. Carney: I think those kids deserved to be judged individually. Some of them are just class clowns. Others have real problems. Surely they don't all deserve the same punishment.

Lisa: I'm Lisa, and I'm a junior. I agree with Mr. Carney. You say that the rules are important, but you just changed the rules without telling anybody. At the rate you're going, who knows what could get us suspended next week?

Narrator: After two hours of discussion, Principal Hodges concludes the meeting.

Principal: Members of a civilized society must follow the rules. And this school is no exception. We must have the power to enforce our rules. However, judging from the range of reactions expressed here tonight, I'm willing to admit that I may have made a mistake. I'm going to form a committee made up of parents, teachers, and possibly even students to study and make recommendations on the policy of zero tolerance.

What do you think the committee should say about the new policy of zero tolerance?